Stag

DARES

DAN BRIDGES

summersdale

STAG DARES

An Hachette UK Company
www.hachette.co.uk

Summersdale Publishers Ltd
Part of Octopus Publishing Group Limited
Carmelite House
50 Victoria Embankment
LONDON
EC4Y 0DZ
UK

www.summersdale.com

Printed and bound in Malta

ISBN: 978-1-78685-544-2

Disclaimer: The publisher urges care and caution in the pursuit of any of the activities represented in this book. This book is intended for use by adults only. The publisher cannot accept any responsibility for the result of the use or misuse of this book or any loss, injury or damage caused thereby. Please drink responsibly.

Substantial discounts on bulk quantities of Summersdale books are available to corporations, professional associations and other organisations. For details contact general enquiries: telephone: +44 (0) 1243 771107 or email: enquiries@summersdale.com.

CONTENTS

ABOUT THE AUTHOR

For years, **Dan Bridges** courageously researched hundreds of stag nights. Thanks to his selfless drinking, streaking and fancy dressing, he was able to create this essential guide. His dedication to his work saw him in line for a knighthood in 2014 before he discovered it was, in fact, just an elaborate prank.

INTRODUCTION

Stag nights are all about having a good time, and you can't spell 'good time' without 'unbridled idiocy'. This chronicle of iniquity has something for everyone: from puerile pranks to devilish dares.

Say goodbye to your dignity, grab your mates and let's stag the hell out of this.

DISCLAIMER

We accept no liability whatsoever for personal injuries (if someone thumps you); loss of clothes or liberty (if you end up in jail); the end of relationships (if your pals fall out with you); or any other negative effects experienced by you or anyone else during or after the carrying out of these dares.

That means you can't sue, you must take full responsibility for your own naughty actions and you can't use this book to defend yourself in court.

A NOTE ON THE POINTS SYSTEM

1-point dares are an appetiser or, perhaps, the absolute ceiling for your designated driver or Johnny-blush-brightly. You can do these in your sleep.

3-point dares might take a little Dutch courage. They'll give your mates a laugh but, mostly, you can do them without talking to real people.

5-point dares require courage, creativity and booze. You'll need to think on your feet and not be afraid to get your pride dirty.

10-point dares do a champion make. Only ye of little shame can hope to score big with these wanton acts of madness. Go big, go forth, and (if undressing in public) go on and on about how it's just a cold evening, that's all.

PRE-DRINKS

Like tackling the loopiest rollercoaster in a theme park first, pre-drinks should get you giddy enough to enjoy what will be, essentially, a night of standing in queues. Let's get the first round in...

1-POINT DARES

Fashion yourself a hat made of loo roll and wear it for at least 30 minutes. Fedora, Stetson, bishop's mitre – other than the total inadequacy of toilet paper, the only limit is your imagination.

DARE 1

Rating: ⭐

DARE 2

Slip bits of paper with bizarre or suggestive messages into the back pockets of three of your group – without them noticing. Later on in the night, mention casually to each of your three victims that you saw someone acting suspiciously behind them.

Rating: ⭐

DARE 3

Pretend to be underwater for 5 minutes. Don't forget to come up for air now and then. Your friends don't need a tragedy on their hands.

Rating: ★

DARE 4

A point for each party member if, between you, you can waste the stag's time on at least four occasions by sending him to investigate outside because, this time, you definitely heard something.

Rating: ⭐

Open beer cans or bottles for all your friends in less than 30 seconds. Bonus point if you do it wearing oven gloves.

DARE **5**

Rating:

DARE 6

When someone goes to the toilet, switch off all the lights. When he comes back, flip the bulbs back on, yell 'SURPRISE!' and mob him like he's a world champion urinator.

Rating: ⭐

Tie your shoelaces together and use them to saw an item of food in half, like you've got a lousy cheesewire between your feet.

DARE **7**

Rating: ⭐

3-POINT DARES

DARE 1

Google Churchill's 'fight on the beaches' speech, cram your mouth with marshmallows and give a dramatic reading to the room without laughing.

Rating: ★ ★ ★

DARE 2

Make a fist and draw a face in marker pen on the side of your hand. Don't drink anything without its permission.

Rating: ★ ★ ★

Every time you take a sip of your drink, you must wink at the stag three times. If he spots you, it's drink-downing time.

DARE 3

Rating: ★ ★ ★

DARE 4

Put a pen in your mouth and draw the woman of your dreams. 'Wow – just look at those erratic curves.'

Rating: ★ ★ ★

Lace the stag's whisky shot with vinegar. As he splutters, pat him on the back and patronisingly tell him that whisky isn't for everyone.

DARE 5

Rating: ★ ★ ★

Speak only in song titles for 5 minutes.

DARE **6**

Rating: ★ ★ ★

5-POINT DARES

Get the stag to pose for 2 minutes while everyone sketches their finest portrait of him. When he's ready to talk to you all again, he can choose a winner.

DARE 1

Rating: ★ ★ ★ ★ ★

DARE 2

Announce that you have organised a game of hide-and-seek with a bottle of premium booze hidden somewhere in the room. Of course, there is no bottle, but watching while they hunt in vain and making encouraging gestures will be great fun.

Rating: ★★★★★

DARE 3

You're not allowed to say 'no' for the next hour. If you do, you have to take a big swig of your drink.

Rating: ★★★★★

DARE 4

Drink all your drinks from a Martini glass. Olive or cocktail umbrella optional.

Rating: ★ ★ ★ ★ ★

Call a work contact
and explain the rules
of Monopoly until
they hang up. If they
don't hang up, you
can move on to Risk.

DARE **5**

Rating: ★★★★★

DARE 6

Got an eye for a bargain? For a fiver or less, buy an utterly useless eBay item and send it to the stag's address. '700 stick-on googly eyes – oh, you shouldn't have.'

Rating: ★★★★★

DARE 7

Build a tower out
of anything you
can find until it's
taller than you are.

Rating: ★ ★ ★ ★ ★

Take 5 minutes away from the stag to gift wrap everyone's shoes. When the taxi arrives, reveal them like it's Christmas morning. For best results, wrap incorrect pairs in matching paper.

DARE 8

Rating: ★ ★ ★ ★ ★

10-POINT DARES

DARE 1

If you have facial hair, shave one side clean off. When someone asks why, tell them you've always wanted a beard but you can't commit.

Rating: ★ ★ ★ ★ ★ ★ ★ ★ ★ ★ ★ ★ ★

DARE 2

Run around the room for a full minute screaming, 'I'M ON INVISIBLE FIRE AND NO ONE WILL BELIEVE ME.'

Rating: ★ ★ ★ ★ ★ ★ ★ ★ ★ ★

DARE 3

Remember your years of 'the floor is lava' training? Do a circuit of the room without touching the ground.

Rating: ★★★★★★★★★★★

SCORES

In this section, you could have up to **95** points on the board.

If you scored **0–35** points: Did you make it to pre-drinks? Did your taxi just sail right past? Do you even care about the stag? DO YOU?

If you notched up **36–70** points: This isn't your first rodeo. Nice work, cowboy – give yourself a pat on the back.

If you hit the big **71+** points: R-E-S-P-E-C-T. You are the best man, in the truest sense of the term.

AT THE PUB

You've reached the Promised Land. You can drink, you can slurp, you can glug. The possibilities are... well, not much more than those, and maybe some cheeky dares. Speaking of which...

1-POINT DARES

DARE 1

Introduce yourself to a stranger, quite seriously, with the line: 'I'm [name, surname] but my enemies call me Bad-to-the-Bone [surname].'

Rating: ★

For the next 30 minutes, you must drink everything from a shoe. When drinking from your shoe, you are to be referred to as 'Lord Biblington'.

DARE **2**

Rating: ⭐

DARE 3

Mumble incoherently to a stranger, finishing with: '... but he's already got a wife and kids in the Philippines that she knows nothing about, so don't tell anyone.'

Rating: ⭐

DARE 4

Tell the bartender: 'In many ways, marriage is a lot like sitting in a bath of beans.' Convince them that it is and you've earned yourself a point.

Rating: ⭐

DARE 5

Exit the toilets rubbing your tongue with your sleeve. Tell a staff member that Mary Berry must've had an off day when she baked that urinal cake.

Rating: ⭐

DARE 6

Drop a coin into a friend's drink and yell: 'Save the Queen!' After they've downed half, begin to cry, hammer the table and wail, 'We're too late – she's dead!'

Rating: ⭐

Persuade a stranger that you've known them for years by asking after their mother's health and pondering whatever happened to that hot girl you both had a crush on.

DARE 7

Rating: ⭐

Lay a friend across some chairs, concentrate hard and proclaim no one can leave until you've made this man levitate.

DARE

Rating: ⭐

3-POINT DARES

DARE 1

Blag a free drink from the bar. If you come back with water or a soft drink, the rest of the night is cancelled.

Rating: ★ ★ ★

DARE 2

Introduce yourself to a stranger as 'Phil McCrevis'. When they laugh, sob and say that it looks like you'll have to move town again and run to the bathroom.

Rating: ★ ★ ★

Mirror everything a stranger does. Bonus point for staring mournfully at their face and lamenting how you've let yourself go.

DARE **3**

Rating:

DARE 4

Convince someone you're a famous scientist. No one knows about science, so they'll be fascinated to hear about your electric windsock.

Rating: ★ ★ ★

Oh goodness, no – the best man has fallen 'ill' and 'can't make' the wedding. Get a stranger to agree to fill in.

DARE **5**

Rating: ★ ★ ★

When you arrive,
introduce yourself
personally to everyone
in the bar. Ev-ery-one.

DARE 6

Rating: ★ ★ ★

5-POINT DARES

DARE 1

Wear your underwear outside your trousers. If someone asks whether that's a bit clichéd for a stag party, smile and say you're not with them.

Rating: ★ ★ ★ ★ ★

DARE 2

Approach a girl at the bar and announce that you're about to show her the best magic trick she's ever seen. Keep her on the edge of her seat for as long as possible without performing any magic whatsoever. If it's more than 5 minutes, the points are yours.

Rating: ★★★★★

DARE 3

Make – and wear – a custom accessory from every pub. Beer-label brooches will add a grand feel to your night. Best one gets a loo-roll rosette.

Rating: ★ ★ ★ ★ ★

DARE 4

Pop your drink down and, without saying anything, lie on the floor and act like a sizzling piece of bacon for 10 seconds. Casually return to a standing position and continue as normal.

Rating: ★★★★★

10-POINT DARES

DARE 1

Find out a stranger's name, go to the toilet and get a mate to write it in pen at the top of your bum. Strike up a conversation about tattoos, and when they ask to see yours…

Rating: ★★★★★★★★★★★★

DARE 2

Ask someone for their autograph. When they ask who you think they are, say you don't know but autographs are hard to get when people find fame so you've decided to plan ahead.

Rating: ★★★★★★★★★★

Remove your underwear without leaving the bar area. Scissors are cheating, as are tear-away stripper pants.

DARE 3

Rating: ★★★★★★★★★★★

DARE 4

One of your crew must strike up conversation with a stranger before dropping in the following: 'Did you know that [your name] has a special talent? It's [whatever comes into their head]. Look, he'll show you right now.' Give it your best shot and the points are yours.

Rating: ★★★★★★★★★★★★

Act out an impromptu death scene. Not elegant, *Titanic*-old-lady death – blubbery, awful *The Notebook* death.

DARE **5**

Rating: ★★★★★★★★★★★★

DARE 6

Stand on a chair, clink a fork against your glass and wait for the attention of the room. Begin, 'Some say animal noises have no place in a moving best man's speech… ' And then, by God, prove them wrong.

Rating: ★★★★★★★★★★

SCORES

You could have trousered **106** points in this section.

If you scored **0-35**: Are you the designated driver? If so, push the car in a lake and enjoy yourself. You literally won't regret it.

If you scored **36-70** points: Is your stag feeling a breeze? Because you're the wind beneath his wings.

If you came in at **71+** points: You are authentic dare royalty. Your telegram from Her Maj is in the post.

OUT AND ABOUT

Until someone does the sensible thing and lines up pubs like beach huts on a shore, you'll still have to walk between them. As chance would have it, we've got dares to keep you merry from door to door.

1-POINT DARES

Treat the first person you see like a guest of honour and welcome them into the group. Get them to come to the next pub with you.

DARE 1

Rating: ⭐

DARE 2

Busk to earn the cash for your next drink. Unleash your inner Cher, and don't sign anything until you talk to your agent.

Rating: ★

DARE 3

Stroll the streets wearing
a finger moustache, and
salute passersby with
a cheerful 'pip pip'.

Rating: ⭐

DARE 4

Encourage big business and raise the profile of your town by buying tubes of toothpaste and drawing a helipad.

Rating: ⭐

Trouble a stranger
for directions to
a local landmark
you've invented.

DARE 5

Rating: ⭐

DARE 6

If some cigarette-toting cowpoke asks you for a light, adopt your most helpful expression, hold up your phone and turn the flashlight function on.

Rating: ★

DARE 7

When you pass a group of people, read the last text message you received, out loud, in the style of a town crier.

Rating: ⭐

3-POINT DARES

Choose two pubs, and sing everything you say as you walk between them.

DARE 1

Rating: ★ ★ ★

DARE 2

Announce that the group must all become statues for 3 minutes. If anyone moves, get very cross, tap your temple and say: 'I didn't say *pretend* to be a statue; I said *become* one.'

Rating: ★ ★ ★

DARE 3

Pose beside a car that matches your personality. Smoulder, pout – you're a tiger, you're a tiger!

Rating: ★ ★ ★

DARE 4

Find someone who looks like a member of the group in 20–30 years' time. There's no bonus point for this bit, but it might help to ask them what to watch out for in the future.

Rating: ★ ★ ★

Find out how many
inflated balloons
you can squeeze
beneath a car. 'Ten',
you say? Yes, ten
sounds about right.

Rating: ★ ★ ★

Call someone who you know will be asleep, and tell them that you just found an acorn that looks like them.

DARE 6

Rating: ★ ★ ★

5-POINT
DARES

DARE 1

Tell someone you fell and hurt yourself, and ask them to inspect you for damage. Point to where you think you might have been 'hurt' by discreetly acting out the full dance to the 'Macarena'.

Rating: ★ ★ ★ ★ ★

DARE 2

Whenever anyone says 'Get down, Mr President' the entire group must surround and protect the stag, Secret Service fashion. Last one in must buy the next round.

Rating: ★ ★ ★ ★ ★

DARE 3

Cover the last 10 yards to the door of a pub in a slow-motion sprint, humming the theme from *Chariots of Fire*.

Rating: ★★★★★

DARE 4

Space yourselves out and have a booze relay race, swigging from your beery baton before it passes from hand to hand.

Rating: ★ ★ ★ ★ ★

Strike up a conversation with someone and see how many facts about avocados you can fit into the exchange before they catch on.

DARE **5**

Rating: ★★★★★

Discover the champion among you with a hearty game of Piggyback Jousting. Get yourselves in the mood by singing the name of the game to the tune of Bob Marley's 'Buffalo Soldier'.

DARE 6

Rating: ★ ★ ★ ★ ★

10-POINT
DARES

DARE 1

Have a full-blown argument with a car. 'ALL YOU WANT TO DO IS SIT IN THE ROAD, CHITTY. WHY CAN'T WE HAVE ADVENTURES LIKE WE USED TO?' Get a mate to film it for posterity – it's sure to be a classic.

Rating: ★ ★ ★ ★ ★ ★ ★ ★ ★ ★

There are lots of pubs, and sometimes it's hard to remember where they are. Ask a stranger for directions, but convey the name of your desired pub through interpretive dance alone.

DARE 2

Rating: ★★★★★★★★★★★★

DARE 3

It's dark, it's late – there could be evil spirits around the next corner. Best scare them away with a loud, improvised haka.

Rating: ★★★★★★★★★★

DARE 4

Eat a whole kebab without using your hands. If you don't know how to eat without using hands, Google 'whales eating' for inspiration.

Rating: ★★★★★★★★★★

DARE 5

Well done – your stag is
having a great time. But
even fun can be tiring.
Do him a solid and, as a
group, carry him the entire
way to the next pub.

Rating: ★ ★ ★ ★ ★ ★ ★ ★ ★ ★ ★ ★

SCORES

You had the chance to reach the heady heights of **105** points in this section, but how did you rate?

If you scored **0–35** points: The important thing is you tried. But the more important thing is you didn't succeed.

If you scored **36–70** points: If drunken pluck was a GCSE (and it never, ever should be), you're a solid 'B'.

If you scored **71+**: There's a plinth in the 'Dare Hall of Fame'. Stand on it. Flex. Let us worship you.

IN THE CLUB

It's the final furlong, the bottom of the ninth, extra time. Don't like sports metaphors? It's… I don't know… the last drop of ink in the printer.

Make yourselves proud.

1-POINT DARES

Wear a sign that says: 'Please look after this bear.' Sit adorably, and wait for your magical new life to begin.

DARE 1

Rating: ⭐

DARE 2

Order your own 'celebrity' cocktail invention. For instance, if it tastes of blackcurrant, you might like to call it 'Danny DeVimto'.

Rating: ⭐

DARE 3

Interrupt a lap dance by asking if the dancer has ever noticed that you only have a lap when you're sitting down.

Rating: ⭐

Tell a toilet attendant
you 'love what they've
done with the place'.

↑

DARE **4**

Rating: ⭐

Order vodka. Wait for them to put it through the till, then adjust your invisible tie like James Bond and add: '… double vodka.'

DARE **5**

Rating: ⭐

DARE 6

Every time a rap song comes on everyone must yell 'This is my jam!' and rap along loudly and enthusiastically.

Rating: ★

3-POINT DARES

DARE 1

Have the group assign you a rude nickname. Now explain 'the story of how you got it' to someone you don't know.

Rating: ★ ★ ★

DARE 2

Use a bad pick-up line on a stranger and try to keep the chat going. For example, 'The only STD I've got is Sexually Transmitted Desire... for you.'

Rating: ★ ★ ★

DARE 3

Blow a kiss to somebody. Act like the kiss didn't budge, and start freaking out about how it won't come off your hand.

Rating: ★ ★ ★

Invent your own euphemism for when 'nature calls', and use it any time you go to wring your mitten.

DARE **4**

Rating: ⭐ ⭐ ⭐

DARE 5

Adopt a French accent and convince a stranger that, while the stag group is genuinely French, you're only pretending because you don't have any friends.

Rating: ★ ★ ★

DARE 6

Ask a member of the bar staff which gins they serve. When they answer, coyly raise an eyebrow and say: 'Are you flirting with me?'

Rating: ★ ★ ★

5-POINT
DARES

DARE 1

Burst from a cubicle in the gents and ask someone at a urinal what year it is. Mutter vaguely that you must have 'overshot' and disappear back inside.

Rating: ★★★★★

DARE 2

Form a human pyramid with the stag at the top. Swear you definitely agreed the person at the highest altitude would buy the next round.

Rating: ★★★★★

DARE 3

Approach a stranger and say, 'Oh, it's a dance-off you want, is it?' Win at all costs.

Rating: ★ ★ ★ ★ ★

Tell someone you're making a documentary about creeping up on people while they're distracted. Watch the nervousness gradually start to take hold.

DARE 4

Rating: ★ ★ ★ ★ ★

Fully commit to the saddest karaoke song you can find. Cry. Dribble.

DARE **5**

Rating: ★ ★ ★ ★ ★

DARE 6

Turn your clothes inside out and wear them around the club. If someone points it out, cunningly reply: 'Am I wearing them inside out? Or are you wearing them the wrong way round?'

Rating: ★ ★ ★ ★ ★

DARE 7

Ask someone to hold your drink, and stay put. See how long you can make them hold it for you.

Rating: ★ ★ ★ ★ ★

10-POINT DARES

DARE 1

Pay the toilet attendant to spray you with two squirts of every scent, proudly proclaiming you are 'a Noah's Ark for cologne'.

Rating: ★★★★★★★★★★

Order a
Cocksucking
Cowboy (Baileys
and butterscotch
schnapps) for the
burliest bloke
at the bar.

DARE **2**

Rating: ★★★★★★★★★★

DARE 3

For your next drama class, you're required to act out the birth of a baby. It's probably too risky to just turn up and hope for the best. Ask a stranger to rate your performance.

Rating: ★ ★ ★ ★ ★ ★ ★ ★ ★ ★

DARE 4

Perform a strip-tease for the stag. It can just be your northern hemisphere that you uncover, but a bonus point for revealing what's south of the equator: the hidden continent known as terra arse-tralis.

Rating: ★★★★★★★★★★

SCORES

How did you do? **99** points were up for grabs.

If you scored **0–35** points: You've scored more or less the same as people who weren't even playing.

If you scored **36–70** points: You've shown some masterful skill tonight. And, if you're all the way up here, that's probably not all you've shown.

If you scored **71+** points: I eagerly await Your Performance Tonight – The Movie. You're a star.